"In *Menopause Moments*, Melani＿ ＿＿ many sides of menopause—the fu＿ ＿＿＿, ᵃⁿᵈ even sweaty moments we women experience as we endure the unique trials of this season of life. Her distinctive voice gives these moments a prayerful touch. I found myself laughing and blushing as so many of her reflections hit home. Hysterically funny and undoubtedly real."

MARY LENABURG, *author of the award-winning* **Be Brave in the Scared**

"Melanie Rigney explores the physical, emotional, and spiritual challenges of menopause with compassion, encouraging women not to view them as setbacks. This journal is packed with gentle, practical tips for embracing and contemplating God's plan in this season of life."

BARB SZYSZKIEWICZ, *editor at CatholicMom.com*

"God loves women in every season of life, but there's an intensity to menopause that ought to give us spiritual pause. And that's exactly what Melanie Rigney recommends. In *Menopause Moments*, she offers readers frequent breaks for prayer and reflection to counterbalance the physical and emotional moments of this ever-changing phase of life."

PAT GOHN, *editor of* **Living Faith: Daily Catholic Devotions**

"*Menopause Moments* is a sweet reprieve, like a Dove chocolate at the end of a grueling day. Any woman of any age, before, during, or long after menopause, will reap the rewards of this helpful handbook of life survival skills."

PATRICIA LORENZ, **Daily Guideposts** *and* **Chicken Soup for the Soul** *contributor and author of 14 books*

"Written with the wit and wisdom that could only come from the heart of a mature woman steeped in God's love and word, this journal at times made me laugh out loud and weep, sometimes both at the same time. *Menopause Moments* serves as a lovely reminder that while the world tries to tell women of a certain age and stage in life they have no worth anymore, God shows us otherwise."

LAURA K. ROLAND, *speaker/blogger; co-founder, Encounter Grace*

"Melanie Rigney has given us a gift. She addresses our awkward concerns and provides reflections and prayers to help us find consolation as well as opportunities for holiness in our suffering. This honest and sometimes poignant book is a great companion in midlife."

MARIA M. JOHNSON, *author of **My Badass Book of Saints: Courageous Women Who Showed Me How to Live***

"Melanie Rigney's *Menopause Moments* invites us to a guided action and reflection toward joy and meaning in the midst of ongoing life changes. It gives us a chance to pause and accept where we are but also to reach for a new insight and understanding of ourselves. These reflections offer an opportunity to embrace and celebrate change."

CHRISTINA PUCHALSKI, MD, OCDS, FACP, FAAHPM, *Professor of Medicine and Health Science; Executive Director, The George Washington University's Institute for Spirituality and Health (GWish)*

menopause moments

A journal for nourishing your mind, body and spirit in midlife

Melanie Rigney

TWENTY-THIRD PUBLICATIONS

twentythirdpublications.com

DEDICATION

To Patricia Lorenz, who shows me how to embrace changes small and large with humor and confidence in God —not to mention grit and gusto!

TWENTY-THIRD PUBLICATIONS
One Montauk Avenue, Suite 200; New London, CT 06320
(860) 437-3012 or (800) 321-0411; www.twentythirdpublications.com

The Scripture passages contained herein are from the *New Revised Standard Version Bible*. Copyright ©1989, by the Division of Christian Education of the National Council of the Churches of Christ in the U.S.A. All rights reserved.

Cover photo: © Izdebska Karolina / Shutterstock.com

ISBN: 978-1-62785-610-2
Printed in the U.S.A.

 A division of Bayard, Inc.

CONTENTS

PREFACE

I was forty-eight years old, editing a book about dog nutrition, when it happened. ZAP! Even though the air conditioning was on that late August afternoon, it felt like my skin was on fire, head to toe. I ran to the bathroom and splashed cold water on my face. It didn't help. I started breathing shallowly—was I having a heart attack? And then, all of a sudden, my body temperature returned to normal.

It was my first hot flash.

If you're nodding in sympathy, this book is for you. I hope you can feel the hug I'm sending.

For me, the runup to menopause lasted only about two years. But I've had friends who have been in transition for five or six years, and more than ten years isn't uncommon. For you, hot flashes might be most challenging; for your best friend, it might be brain fog. Add in changes in your parents' health, kids hitting puberty with their own fluctuating hormones, hitting your stride—or failing to—in your career, and some days, you may feel like you're all alone.

This journal's purpose is to show you you're never alone, and maybe to make you laugh a little. There's a short reflection for each entry, along with a verse to contemplate, an action item, and a spark for reflecting or praying. You can start with day one, or thumb through to find the page you need that particular day. Either way, I hope you feel refreshed and more confident in your future, yourself, and your faith.

"You are observing special days, and months, and seasons, and years," Paul wrote in Galatians 4:10. My prayer for you is that you don't lose the joy moments during these special days, uncertain though they feel at times. Take comfort in knowing that God's love for you never is.

menopause
moments

Light Sleep, Dark Nights

*"Come to me, all you that are weary and are carrying
heavy burdens, and I will give you rest."*

MATTHEW 11:28

You toss. You turn. When you do fall asleep, the slightest noise brings you back to wide-eyed wakefulness. You go to bed tired, and you wake up tired. There are so many things to try—hormone replacement therapy, melatonin, white noise, exercise, boring memory challenges (remember every teacher you ever had, starting with kindergarten)—but some nights, not one of them works. And you know what sleepless nights can lead to: cranky, restless days.

There's no one, surefire way to overcome disrupted sleep. Thankfully, there is one surefire way to keep it from turning you into a total grouch. Instead of fretting, offer up your sleeplessness. Get out of bed and sit in a comfy chair with your Bible or other spiritual reading for a half hour. Pray the Rosary, the Divine Mercy Chaplet, or have a spontaneous conversation with God. Your body may still be tired, but your spirit will be refreshed. As Jesus told us with so much love, "Come to me, all you that are weary and carrying heavy burdens, and I will give you rest."

ACTION

Consider keeping a journal this week of what you eat and do before bed, your bedtime, and how you sleep to see if there are some patterns. Does it help when you incorporate prayer into your bedtime preparations?

FOR PRAYER AND REFLECTION

Dear Saint Joseph, God entrusted to you the protection of Mary and Jesus. So that I may sleep and be prepared to do the Almighty's work tomorrow, I entrust to you this worry of mine:

Friends, New and Old

*Do not abandon old friends,
for new ones cannot equal them.
A new friend is like new wine;
when it has aged, you can drink it with pleasure.*

SIRACH 9:10

You've had your "posse" for years. Maybe it's the moms with whom you share school or after-school event carpooling, or maybe it's the other women on your street with whom you've organized years of block parties and progressive dinners. Or maybe it's the friends you've made at work or through professional organizations. They haven't changed, but you feel stale. You wonder if it's time to shake up your friendships a little—then feel guilty and ungrateful for thinking about it.

As your life changes, so do your friendships. You're not betraying anyone if you choose to spend less time with a particular circle of friends to broaden things out through a new prayer group, or perhaps a support group for an ache in your life. You can tend both old and new friendships, knowing, as Ben Sira wrote, a new friendship when aged with time is something "you can drink…with pleasure."

ACTION

How can you, as the saying goes, make new friends but keep the old? Which friendships do you find to be a drag on your joy? Are there women at your parish, in your neighborhood, or at work you'd like to get to know better?

FOR PRAYER AND REFLECTION

Why do I keep investing time and effort in a friendship where there is no reciprocation?

Sweats and Flashes

Does not the dew give relief from the scorching heat?
So a word is better than a gift.
SIRACH 18:16

You probably remember your first hot flash or night sweat. Maybe it shocked you, the way it came on suddenly and ended just as suddenly. A study from WebMD and HealthyWomen found that that was the first sign of menopause for more than 60 percent of women. Knowing you have a lot of company probably doesn't help much, though. At night, you kick the covers on and off, disturbing your husband if you're married. During the day, you're always the one at home or in the office who wants to turn up the air conditioning—for a few minutes, anyway, until this episode passes.

Feeling like you're inside a furnace isn't pleasant. Sometimes, deep breathing helps. You might find it helpful as you breathe out to give thanks for the unique blessings you have received as a woman—and those to come in the future. Truly, gratitude is a form of the dew that Ben Sira had in mind that gives "relief from the scorching heat."

ACTION

Talk with friends about the blessings of being a woman—of giving birth, of raising a family, of nurturing a marriage or business, of caregiving. Men are capable of doing much of this, but women have a particular gift for mothering of all sorts. What are you doing or what will you do to share this genius with the next generation?

FOR PRAYER AND REFLECTION

Three things that make me happy I'm a woman are:

Shifts of Time

Therefore my heart is glad, and my soul rejoices;
my body also rests secure.

PSALM 16:9

You unpack that linen dress you love to wear in the summer—except now, it looks stretched across your hips. You order a new pair of pants in the same size and style you've worn for years—except now, your butt looks huge and you have trouble buttoning or zipping them. The scale confirms you haven't gained weight. Call it gravity; call it the shifts of time. Some of those pounds have headed south, right where you don't need them.

Looking at your body can be downright uncomfortable, regardless of how much you exercise or how careful you are about what you eat. While giving up and binging on a box of cookies or a bag of chips isn't healthy, God finds beauty in your appearance even if you go up a size or two. As the psalmist wrote, when the Lord is before us, "my body also rests secure."

ACTION

It just might be time to switch up your workout routine, possibly including more activities to keep your bones strong. Talk with your doctor or a trainer about whether a change would be good for your body and spirit. When the exercise of either gets to be too rote, it's easy to get bored and out of shape.

FOR PRAYER AND REFLECTION

I'll take a 10-minute walk today on a different route than I usually do, and be present to God's wonders by watching for:

Counting the Hairs

"Are not two sparrows sold for a penny? Yet not one of them will fall to the ground apart from your Father. And even the hairs of your head are all counted. So do not be afraid; you are of more value than many sparrows."

MATTHEW 10:29–31

Your hair was your "crowning" glory. Sometimes, you even complained about how much time it took to dry and style it. But now, you notice a lot more in your brush or comb than ever before. You've checked with a physician, and there's nothing wrong with you beyond getting older—and, possibly, female-pattern hair loss. But it's not like your dad's, your brother's, or your husband's. Your hair is thinning out all over the crown of your head.

You have options; there are topical solutions that purport to thicken up your hair, and there's always the try-a-new-style-to-hide-it approach. While you may feel less physically attractive these days, and perhaps a little embarrassed about finding yourself so concerned about this, take comfort in God's love, for as Jesus said, "even the hairs of your head are all counted."

ACTION

Look at a photo from a good hair day. Maybe it was your high school or college graduation, or your wedding day. Your hair may have looked great, but you've undoubtedly grown in wisdom since that time. Write a letter to that "before" you to share what you wish you'd known then that gives you comfort now.

FOR PRAYER AND REFLECTION

Today, I'll reflect on an experience where I couldn't see God at first, but that turned out to be a blessing.

Reading Minds

Jesus stood still and called them, saying,
"What do you want me to do for you?" They said
to him, "Lord, let our eyes be opened."
MATTHEW 20:32–33

You rejoin your family after prayer group. The dinner dishes are still on the kitchen counter. Your husband's watching football or baseball. The kids are on their phones. Or, everyone's supposed to take turns cleaning out the refrigerator at work, but you always end up doing it. Can't anyone see that you need a break from being the Responsible One, just for one day?

You might think it's obvious, but your family and coworkers don't. It could be they think you actually enjoy doing particular tasks. Or, could it be that you're so exacting in the way you want things done that others have given up on pleasing you? They might not ask you Jesus' question—"What do you want me to do for you?"—but things may improve if you ask for help. You may find out that a clean work refrigerator doesn't matter to anyone else, but a smile and "good morning" do.

ACTION

None of us can read minds. How can you ask people for the help and support you need from them—or ask them what they want from you?

FOR PRAYER AND REFLECTION

Jesus, help me to be a servant in your image today.
Open my eyes to what someone I find difficult to love
in the moment needs from me.

Erased

*Rather, let your adornment be the inner self
with the lasting beauty of a gentle and quiet spirit,
which is very precious in God's sight.*

1 PETER 3:4

A purple streak here, a pink streak there. Maybe you've gone auburn for the winter or added highlights for the summer. It can be fun to express yourself through a change in hair color. But that gray you're seeing isn't much fun, and plus, it's wiry and coarse and has a will of its own. You ponder the cost of having it professionally colored vs. learning to do it yourself vs. letting it go and risking the possibility of being seen as "old," whatever that is.

Graying hair is one of the most obvious outward signs of aging for most of us. There's nothing wrong with coloring your locks, or with celebrating each and every gray or white one. Whatever you decide, remember that the most precious adornment to God is "the lasting beauty of a gentle and quiet spirit."

ACTION

To color or not to color? Consider what your mom, grandmothers, and other beloved older relatives did with their hair. Then reflect on what you treasure most about them. Hint: it's probably not their hair, but their hearts and hugs.

FOR PRAYER AND REFLECTION

The most important thing my mom or someone who's like a mom taught me is:

Irregular Grace

For everything there is a season,
and a time for every matter under heaven.
ECCLESIASTES 3:1

These days, you don't leave the house without a pad or tampon. That cycle—four days, thirty days apart—that you took for granted for years is no more. Your periods last longer with a heavier flow or are shorter and lighter but seem to start when they please, twenty-five days apart one time, thirty-five days the next. Everyone—your physician, your internet search, your relatives, your older friends—all tell you to get used to it; it's natural. That may be, but the uncertainty is hard—as may be the awareness that your childbearing days are nearing an end.

Maybe you loved being pregnant, or maybe it was difficult for you; maybe you haven't given birth. Still, it's unsettling to have this very real sign that soon that won't be a possibility. Mourn that loss, but also have confidence that the future holds joy in unexpected ways because "for everything there is a season."

ACTION

Think about "endings" you've experienced that turned into joy: Graduating high school, perhaps, and moving to a new world at college. Moving with your family to a new neighborhood or town where you built strong friendships. Savor your unknown future, confident in God's timing.

FOR PRAYER AND REFLECTION

The "ending" in my life that turned out to be
a moment of grace was:

Something Old, Something New

I am about to do a new thing;
now it springs forth, do you not perceive it?

ISAIAH 43:19

You go to a family funeral and realize you don't know how many brothers or sisters your grandparents had and think it'd be fun to get into genealogy. A woman in your prayer group brings her knitting, and you remember you loved the time you spent on crafts before the kids were born. A new friend is a jogger, and you wonder if it's too late for you to give it a try.

This is a perfect time to get back to an old hobby, or to start a new one. You've reached the point in life where it's less important to do something perfectly, and more important to spend free time on activities you enjoy or find challenging in a positive way. What is that thing? Do you not perceive it, as Isaiah wrote?

ACTION

Maybe it's sculpting, maybe it's skydiving, or maybe it's gardening. There's something you're itching to do, or get back to. Give yourself permission to look into scratching that itch.

FOR PRAYER AND REFLECTION

Today I'll scratch that itch by:

Yikes!

The human body is a fleeting thing,
but a virtuous name will never be blotted out.

SIRACH 41:11

There's a feeling of *whoosh*, and you know you have to pee—right now. You, who used to be able to hike or sit in meetings for hours on end without feeling any bladder discomfort. Even if you scout out available bathrooms when you enter a location, you can still find it a challenge to hold on. Frequent, urgent urination can be linked to your estrogen levels reducing as part of menopause. It also can be related to the strain vaginal childbirth puts on pelvic floor muscles. Regardless of the cause, it can be pretty embarrassing.

What's to be done? You've likely heard of Kegel exercises and may already be doing them. Experts recommend against reducing your liquid intake as a possible solution. There's always carrying a pad. But perhaps part of the answer lies in not escalating the situation by obsessing about it. Our earthly bodies weren't made to carry us into eternity. It's wiser, then, to focus on the bigger picture—our virtuous name, which as Ben Sira said "will never be blotted out."

ACTION

Take the long view with your body during this time that it's behaving in new ways. Be gentle and patient with yourself, one day at a time.

FOR PRAYER AND REFLECTION

Here are three ways I can quiet my anxiety about this change:

Anointment

She removed the sackcloth she had been wearing,
took off her widow's garments, bathed her body with water,
and anointed herself with precious ointment.

JUDITH 10:3

You love that twinkle in your husband's eye as much as you ever did. His smile still dazzles you. The two of you have more alone time now that the kids are off to college or involved in evening activities that don't require your constant supervision. But as attracted to him as you still are, your body and your brain aren't on the same page anymore. Your dryness makes things uncomfortable for you both. You talk to each other about everything—except this.

It's true that you lose estrogen pre- and post-menopause, and that can result in vaginal dryness. It has nothing to do with not finding your husband as sexy as you once did. Don't be afraid to tell him that. Some couples incorporate lubricants into their lovemaking to help with the discomfort; some women use moisturizers. Setting the scene also could make a difference; consider the example of Judith as she set forth to deliver God's people: she "bathed her body with water, and anointed herself with precious ointment."

ACTION

Prepare for an evening with your husband in the way you did when you were dating. Single? Divorced? Widowed? Pamper yourself and dress up for a date with yourself or friends.

FOR PRAYER AND REFLECTION

I'll write someone a love note today—not an email, not a text, but a handwritten note.

Brain Fog

Can a woman forget her nursing child,
or show no compassion for the child of her womb?
Even these may forget, yet I will not forget you.

ISAIAH 49:15

You walk into a room—but don't recall why you did. You used to be able to remember a half-dozen items to buy at the store—now you need to write them down (and not lose the list). Maybe you lose track during the Lord's Prayer or Hail Mary. You secretly fear that maybe you're experiencing the signs of early dementia. Most likely, you're not; it's a "brain fog" that most women at your age experience. The good news that memory does seem to resolve to a large degree with time.

There are plenty of ways you can cope with brain fog. Some experts say a brisk walk, less sugar, or better sleep habits can help. There's nothing wrong with living your life at 60 miles an hour instead of 75. Don't beat yourself up over a missed grocery item or the failure to remember an acquaintance's name or even a beloved prayer. As God said through the prophet Isaiah, you may forget, "yet I will not forget you."

ACTION

Write out in longhand—not on computer—the words to your favorite prayer, or other spiritual aid that's important to you, maybe something from a favorite saint. After you've written it, read it out loud, pausing and thinking about each word.

FOR PRAYER AND REFLECTION

What can I do to remember God today,
since the Almighty never forgets me?

Unfinished Business

For surely I know the plans I have for you,
says the Lord, plans for your welfare and not
for harm, to give you a future with hope.

JEREMIAH 29:11

There's so much positive in your life, but all you can focus on are the things undone. You're facing the fact that you'll never give birth, or that your family is likely complete. You're not where you thought you'd be in your career; that corner office isn't in the cards. You love your neighborhood and your home, but it's not what you dreamed of back in your twenties. You're not exactly sure you even want to be in that dream place anymore, but you know it's not going to happen.

There's a mourning that comes when you realize some of your old dreams will never come to be. But this time also has a way of making you realize the only thing you could ever truly count on was God, and that the Almighty's plans always have been and always will be "not for harm (but) to give you a future with hope."

ACTION

Pull out the high school or college yearbook, or your diary from a decade ago or more. What did you worry about then that never transpired? How can you now see God's hand even in what were disappointments at that time?

FOR PRAYER AND REFLECTION

I'll keep my eyes forward today by:

Squeeze Play Redux

Out of Zion, the perfection of beauty,
God shines forth.

PSALM 50:2

A zit? Seriously? You thought you'd left that all behind in your teens or early twenties. Your acne isn't as bad as it was back then, but why is this happening? What's more, now you're also finding pimples on your scalp. Gross!

Yep. For some women in menopause transition, adult acne becomes a thing, due to those fluctuating hormones. Or, if you've recently changed creams, sunscreens, or cosmetics to deal with other symptoms, they could be the issue. There's also stress, you know, which also probably caused you to break out before a big date or test back in the day. As you seek out the cause and possible solutions, remember that pimples or no pimples, "God shines forth" through you to others if you let that happen.

ACTION

Remember what your mom used to say when you squeezed pimples as a teenager? "Keep your hands off your face!" That's still good advice. When you're tempted to squeeze today, distract yourself by picking up your Bible or other spiritual resource, or doing something small and quick to help someone else.

FOR PRAYER AND REFLECTION

I'll journal today about one thing I like about my face, even if it takes me a while to decide what it is.

Loose Ends

You are observing special days,
and months, and seasons, and years.
GALATIANS 4:10

You complained as much as anyone else, but secretly, you liked being the room mother, the Girl Scout leader, the organizer of the parish ministry fair, or the chair of the office holiday party committee. But now, things are changing. Your children are out of grade school, or maybe there've been less than subtle hints it's time for "new blood" in parish or work activities you lead. You're starting to realize how difficult it is to move away from the place at the head table, and you wonder what you'll do with your time.

There's a sense of loss, to be sure, when our service in a particular ministry or role is done. It's okay to be a little sad about it. But the joyful thing is that there are new opportunities ahead. Take comfort in knowing that even now, "you are observing special days, and months, and seasons, and years."

ACTION

Check out the parish website, the office bulletin board, or your neighborhood's social media channel. Who needs the help God has suited you to provide?

FOR PRAYER AND REFLECTION

I'll make a list of three things I love to do and am good at, and new ways in which I could use them to God's glory.

The Weight

*For she is a reflection of eternal light,
a spotless mirror of the working of God,
and an image of his goodness.*
WISDOM 7:26

When you first moved away from home, you may have put on the "freshman 15" whether or not you went to college. You know, those pounds that come with drinking and eating a little too much. But you regained at least a modicum of self-control, and until now, have more or less maintained your weight with a balance of healthy eating and physical activity. But these days, you don't like the way the scale is trending, no matter how much you cut back on calories and how many extra minutes you add to the elliptical.

Your metabolism is slowing down, but there are ways to battle those extra pounds: be even more vigilant about making your calories count with nutrient-rich foods (and, sad to say, maybe that nightly glass of wine needs to be cut back). You can also work in some additional activity by parking in the far corner of the grocery lot or taking the stairs rather than the elevator. Still, it's important to remember that what goes into our hearts and souls is even more important: "for she is a reflection of eternal light, a spotless mirror of the working of God, and an image of his goodness."

ACTION

Look at your body in the mirror, not just the bigger tummy. Look at the laugh lines around your eyes and remember the joys that resulted in their acquisition. Look at the light God put in your eyes. Give yourself a hug.

FOR PRAYER AND REFLECTION

Today, my prayer of gratitude will include:

Balancing Act

God is my shield,
who saves the upright in heart.

PSALM 7:10

You weren't a star gymnast in school, but you've never felt as prone to lose your balance as you do today. Sometimes you've felt a little dizzy as you went from lying down or sitting to a standing position. And this doesn't always seem to be related to a bad night's rest or a hot flash.

A recent study found that as many as a third of women going through menopausal transition have occasional balance problems. In addition to hot flashes and a lack of sleep, the causes may include a change in the way your body is responding to insulin, or inner ear issues that may be related to hormonal changes. Do talk to your doctor before you experience a serious fall. While your posture changes may need to become more intentional, remaining "upright in heart" with God as your shield should be even more intentional.

ACTION

Try walking in a straight line, toe to heel, for thirty steps, or standing on one leg for thirty seconds. Consider praying a Hail Mary to ease any anxiety as you do so. (It's also a great way to estimate thirty seconds.)

FOR PRAYER AND REFLECTION

I'll set a one-week goal—spiritual, physical, or emotional—for getting some things in my life in balance.

The Last Nerve

As God's chosen ones, holy and beloved,
clothe yourselves with compassion, kindness,
humility, meekness, and patience.

COLOSSIANS 3:12

That habit your husband has of mispronouncing a newscaster's name used to amuse you, but some days now, it sends you into a fury. Your best friend's propensity to be ten minutes late for everything is something you've accepted for years, but you blew up at her about it yesterday. Will the patient you ever come back?

Hormonal changes, including disrupted sleep patterns, can wreak havoc with your mood. Words you usually wouldn't say rush to your lips and sometimes can't be stopped. Journaling about the situation can help, and so can giving yourself even a 30-second "timeout" before you respond when you're feeling irritable. Remember, you are called to clothe yourself "with compassion, kindness, humility, meekness, and patience."

ACTION

Write down the three things that annoy you most about your spouse or best friend or child. Then write down ten things you love about this person. Keep the list with you for the rest of the week.

FOR PRAYER AND REFLECTION

Jesus, help me to be patient today with:

That Look

The heart changes the countenance,
either for good or for evil.

SIRACH 13:25

A few years ago, you got a kick out of the public focus on what we'll call resting witch face. You know, that non-smiling look primarily women, including celebrities, get accused of. But now you find your family and friends asking you what's wrong. Nothing, you say, why do you ask? And they tell you that you look upset. When you see photos, you have to agree.

If you're tired of people saying you should smile more, join the club. This is your dispensation to arrange your face however you like. But consider whether being present in the particular conversation instead of thinking about your to-do list or what you're going to say even before the other person finishes a thought might help with "that look," for "the heart changes the countenance, either for good or for evil."

ACTION

Be in the moment as much as possible today, whether it's praying, having a conversation, or doing work around the house. Check out your expression now and then during this time.

FOR PRAYER AND REFLECTION

I'll think today about a step I can take toward not judging people based on their facial expression.

Less Than Womanly?

You are stately as a palm tree,
and your breasts are like its clusters.
SONG OF SOLOMON 7:7

Your breasts are, well, sagging. Whether or not you breastfed, they seem to be flattening out and heading south instead of being perky. And that bra size you've worn for years? The cups just don't fit right anymore.

Maybe it's more about the memories than the actual sag. Your breasts provided nourishment and love to your children during nursing. That closeness you feel to them and to your husband doesn't have to change with time. Single or married, you're no less of a woman because your chest looks different due to time, lumpectomy, or mastectomy. Remember, as a beloved daughter of God, "you are stately as a palm tree, and your breasts are like its clusters."

ACTION

Breasts are an outward sign of your womanhood. So are kindness
and compassion. Consider how you can keep the latter two from
sagging.

FOR PRAYER AND REFLECTION

*Today, I'll write about a way I can show in actions and
words my status as a stately daughter of the King.*

Transitions

Remember that it was of your parents you were born;
how can you repay what they have given to you?
SIRACH 7:28

Your parents or other well-loved family or friends in the generation before yours are changing. Maybe your mom has retired from work outside the home and is texting or calling you every hour. Or maybe Dad recently lost his walking or card-playing buddy and wants more of your time. You love them but you truly don't have any more to give.

Life changes in your sixties and seventies are hard too, as it becomes all too apparent there's less sand left in the hourglass than has flowed through. Consider helping your beloved seniors find new ways of connecting with others; you don't necessarily have to rearrange your entire life, just provide support as they rearrange theirs. As Ben Sira wrote, "Remember that it was of your parents you were born."

ACTION

Help one of your parents, or someone old enough to be your parent, check out volunteer activities in their parish or community or with a hobby or other interest group. Who knows, you may find something that speaks to you as well.

FOR PRAYER AND REFLECTION

I am most grateful to my parents for:

Oh, Snap!

He touched her hand, and the fever left her,
and she got up and began to serve him.

MATTHEW 8:15

Why is it that one of your fingernails breaks the day after a manicure, regardless of whether you go to a salon or give yourself one? Repair products seldom work that well. Remember the days when you could hike or play tennis or do housework or a million other things and your nails were like sturdy soldiers? It's aggravating—and potentially, expensive.

Brittle nails can be part of the transition to menopause. But they don't much matter when it comes to cradling babies, bathing a sick person, helping out at the community garden, or typing up notes so you can participate fully in your next prayer group meeting. Remember, when Jesus healed Peter's mother-in-law, he wasn't concerned about how beautiful her nails were: "he touched her hand, and the fever left her, and she got up and began to serve him."

ACTION

Consider organizing a girls' evening in, where you and your friends give each other manicures, and talk about how your hands can be used to help others.

FOR PRAYER AND REFLECTION

I pray today for the grace and self-awareness to value my hands for what they can do more than for how they look.

Counting Our Days

*So teach us to count our days
that we may gain a wise heart.*

PSALM 90:12

Maybe it was the big 4-0, or the big 5-0. Maybe it was your twentieth wedding anniversary, or the certificate you received for twenty years with your employer. Maybe it was your son or daughter turning thirteen. But all these numbers overwhelm you and make you wish you could do something, anything, to slow down time. You feel helpless when you know you should feel like celebrating.

Sure, there are always twenty-four hours in a day, seven days in a week, and so on. But they all seem to pass faster as we age, and that can be depressing. Consider looking at the positives that come with these milestones rather than mourning time's passage. Let's "count our days that we may gain a wise heart."

ACTION

Pick out a milestone that's coming up. Make a collage of photos that honor this passage, or journal about how you have grown in faith since five or ten years ago—or what you can do to grow in the coming year.

FOR PRAYER AND REFLECTION

Today I'll write three "impossible" personal prayers—and put them away for a month and then see how God has answered them.

Kids These Days

"His mercy is for those who fear him from generation to generation."

LUKE 1:50

Your son refuses to go to Mass. Your daughter pierced her nose—without your permission. The checker scanning your groceries stops to text someone in the middle of the order. The summer intern in your office is wearing what look like pajamas. You feel like you've become your parents or maybe your grandparents. What's wrong with kids these days?

Well, actually, maybe nothing. You don't know what beats in the heart of the checker, and it might not be your responsibility to enforce a dress code with the intern. As for your son and daughter, you've planted the seed of faith and propriety, and a conversation with questions and without raised voices might be in order. Take comfort in knowing this isn't all on your shoulders, for "his mercy is for those who fear him from generation to generation."

ACTION

Have a conversation with one of your children or another young person, not about dress codes or social media use but about his or her dreams for the future. Don't point out the holes in his or her logic; listen and ask questions.

FOR PRAYER AND REFLECTION

I'll write today about the joy—and fear—I felt when I first held my child or got my first job, and how my faith helped me celebrate the joy, and settle the fear.

Crying Game

"For the Lamb at the center of the throne will be their shepherd, and he will guide them to springs of the water of life, and God will wipe every tear from their eyes."

REVELATION 7:17

Anything, it seems, can bring you to tears—missing a traffic light, reading a recipe, tying your shoes. You don't understand why this is; you've always enjoyed a good cry at a sad movie or a happy event such as a wedding. But now, you always seem to be on the edge of a crying jag.

Your hormone levels are in flux during the transition to menopause, and some highs and lows are natural. Tears aren't always a bad thing. Consider turning to Scripture in those moments when the small annoyances of life seem overwhelming. Remember, God is in everything and "will wipe every tear from their eyes."

ACTION

Cry it out with Mama Mary. Feel her confusion at Gabriel's appearance and at the Presentation. Feel her sorrow at the Crucifixion. Feel her joy in seeing the risen Jesus.

FOR PRAYER AND REFLECTION

Today I'll write out by hand a Scripture verse that gives me faith and confidence when I'm feeling overwhelmed.

In the Bones

The Lord will guide you continually,
and satisfy your needs in parched places,
and make your bones strong;
and you shall be like a watered garden,
like a spring of water, whose waters never fail.

ISAIAH 58:11

You look at photos of your parents' or grandparents' wedding, and wow, Mom or Grandma sure looks a lot shorter now. Maybe your own grip isn't as strong as it once was, or you took a minor fall recently and ended up with a fracture. What's up with your bones?

Reduced bone density can leave you leaving physically fragile. If you're in a volunteer ministry that involves a lot of standing, such as helping shoppers at a food pantry, consider asking if you could take a turn sitting and welcoming people as they arrive. As you tend to your tibia, fibula, and other physical bones' strength, remember the path to strong spiritual bones: "the Lord will guide you continually, and satisfy your needs in parched places."

ACTION

Physical exercise can strengthen your joints and spine. Consider offering up each set of repetitions for a member of your family or faith community so that you can build your spirit and body at the same time.

FOR PRAYER AND REFLECTION

*Today, I'll ask God to replenish both
my spirit and my aching joints.*

Shh...It's a Secret

"For there is nothing to be hidden, except to be disclosed;
nor is anything secret, except to come to light."

MARK 4:22

You quickly close your browser when your husband walks in because you don't want him to see you're searching for information on menopause. You're on the treadmill and hide the web pages you printed out on the topic inside a bigger fashion magazine. You talk about everything with your best friend—everything, that is, except your thinning hair and dryness "down there."

Our society does worship youth, but that doesn't make aging sinful. This is another passage in your earthly life, and nothing you have to be ashamed of or embarrassed about. If you feel that way, talk with Jesus about it, "for there is nothing to be hidden, except to be disclosed, nor is anything secret, except to come to light."

ACTION

Think back to another "embarrassing" time, such as puberty or pregnancy. What do you wish you had celebrated rather than hidden about those experiences, and how can you put that realization to work today?

FOR PRAYER AND REFLECTION

*I'll pray for God's help in understanding that
all these changes are not shameful, but part of the loving
Father's plan in preparing me for eternal life.*

Out of Focus

Listen, and hear my voice;
Pay attention, and hear my speech.

ISAIAH 28:23

You went through that new recipe at least four times, only to find out midway through the preparation that it's supposed to marinate overnight, so it won't be ready for dinner after all. You start home after Mass, and realize you have no recollection of the homily. What's happened to your focus?

Short-term memory and concentration problems aren't uncommon in women your age, though if you get too concerned, it's a good idea to talk with your doctor. Physical activity and working your brain in new ways may help. It might also surprise you how much you'll absorb if you slow down and listen to God. As Isaiah wrote, "Pay attention, and hear my speech."

ACTION

Read out loud your favorite Scripture or saint's quote. Close your eyes and breathe. Then open them and try saying it from memory. Don't beat yourself up if it takes a few tries to do this.

FOR PRAYER AND REFLECTION

Today, I'll try to get through a morning or afternoon focusing on God's to-do list for me, not my own. What is God asking of me today?

That Burn

For no one ever hates his own body, but he nourishes and
tenderly cares for it, just as Christ does for the church.

EPHESIANS 5:29

At first you think you must have pulled a muscle or stretched funny, but then you realize you haven't. But that throbbing pain or burning sensation in your breast is troublesome, though it only lasts for a few seconds. And you notice when you do your monthly check for lumps, the girls are more sensitive these days.

You probably think the worst: breast cancer. It's never a good idea to ignore a lump or other significant change in your breasts. Still, one study found tender breasts are a pretty typical sign of perimenopause, and burning and throbbing aren't unusual either. Consider taking a pain reliever as needed. Toughing it out isn't required, "for no one ever hates his own body, but he nourishes and tenderly cares for it, just as Christ does for the church."

ACTION

Treat yourself to a nice, long, soaking bath or shower, or be generous with the use of your favorite body lotion. There's nothing wrong with a little self-pampering now and then.

FOR PRAYER AND REFLECTION

I'll journal today about three ways I can better use my brain or body to say yes to God's desires for me.

Pillow Face

The steadfast love of the Lord never ceases,
his mercies never come to an end;
they are new every morning;
great is your faithfulness.

LAMENTATIONS 3:22–23

You actually kind of like those smile crinkles around your eyes. Then you started seeing a few other wrinkles on your face when you first woke up, but by the time you were brushing your teeth after breakfast, they were gone. That is, until the day they weren't. It feels like you're looking at your mother's or grandmother's face instead of your own. You know that's an exaggeration, but it's how it feels.

There's some evidence that sleeping on your back can slow down the development of wrinkles, even as your estrogen level goes down. That, however, can be hard to do if you've spent a lifetime as a side or tummy sleeper. Consider learning to accept this process, knowing that the Lord's mercies "are new every morning," additional wrinkles or not.

ACTION

Start your morning by examining the mercies you received yester-day, and offer gratitude for God's abounding love for you. Resolve to worry about wrinkles another day.

FOR PRAYER AND REFLECTION

*In three ways, I will pass on in my interactions
with others God's mercies bestowed on me.*

If It Sounds Too Good to Be True

You desire truth in the inward being;
therefore teach me wisdom in my secret heart.

PSALM 51:6

A year or two ago, you laughed at those ads in your social media feeds about products that melt away belly fat or wrinkles or banish hot flashes. But now that you're into your menopause transition, those promises hit a little closer to home. Could they really advertise those pills and creams if they haven't helped some people?

Unfortunately, yes "they" could—until they get caught, which means people get taken for hundreds or thousands of dollars. The evil one likes to strike where you are most vulnerable, and right now, that may be your body. Remember that, as the psalmist wrote, to turn to your "secret heart" for God's wisdom.

ACTION

Before you sign on for a "sure-fire remedy," consider how much money such a regimen would cost you in the coming six months or year. Is there a way that money might be better spent through a charity or ministry?

FOR PRAYER AND REFLECTION

Jesus, help me to be less concerned about the
outside and more about the inside of me today.

What's All the Fuss?

Without counsel, plans go wrong,
but with many advisers they succeed.
To make an apt answer is a joy to anyone,
and a word in season, how good it is!

PROVERBS 15:22–23

Someone gave you this book as a gift, or maybe you bought it out of curiosity. Really, you don't see what all the fuss about. You've had a hot flash or two, and your body's shifting about a bit, but that comes with age, right? It's hard to listen to your friends complain as if they're the first women in the world to approach menopause.

It's time to count your blessings—and be a friend. After all, they've probably listened to you about anxiety over your family or job or health. You don't have to be waking up drenched in sweat to sympathize with your bestie who is. Just saying, "That sounds hard" may be exactly what she needs from you. As Proverbs advises, "to make an apt answer is a joy to anyone, and a word in season, how good it is!"

ACTION

The next time a friend starts talking about graying hair or hot flashes or wrinkles, don't discount her concerns or offer solutions. Ask her about what's behind her concerns. Go below the surface.

FOR PRAYER AND REFLECTION

Today, I'll listen to someone's fears and concerns without judging or inserting my own experience.

Hallelujah!

If you follow my statutes and keep my commandments
and observe them faithfully, I will give you your rains
in their season, and the land shall yield its produce,
and the trees of the field shall yield their fruit.

LEVITICUS 26:3–4

Honestly, you're excited about this stage of the journey. Perhaps you're looking forward to the time that natural family planning doesn't dictate the times for your physical intimacy with your husband. It's neat to see what interesting people your high school and college age children have become. And you're a bit relieved that the days of organizing the carpooling to activities are coming to a close. If you're single, maybe you view this time as your final big push for promotion at work, or to get involved in a new-to-you volunteer activity because professional demands are under control.

You rock, woman! You are embracing life as God means you to do, confident that when you obey and are faithful to the Almighty's desires for you, "the trees of the field shall yield their fruit."

ACTION

God is good—yesterday, today, and tomorrow. While it's good to embrace the future, what can you do today, not tomorrow, to show your trust?

FOR PRAYER AND REFLECTION

Today, I'll dance in the rain, on the sidewalk,
or in my living room to celebrate God's goodness.

Dry Eyes

"Come," my heart says, "seek his face!"
Your face, Lord, do I seek.

PSALM 27:8

Where did that bottle of eyedrops go? Your eyes feel scratchy and dry so often these days. You've always practiced good eye hygiene—regular breaks from your screen, not wearing your contacts beyond the prescribed number of hours. You've even tried going back to glasses, but that hasn't helped much.

People have a group of hormones called androgens that include testosterone and may have a role in tear production. Since you have less testosterone than your husband, brother, or male friends, you guessed it, you're more likely to have dry eyes than they are. It's strange, isn't it, to go from dry eye to tears in the same day? As you work through this physical issue, continue to "seek his face"; you don't need eyes to see it.

ACTION

If you typically spend your prayer time by reading Scripture or other faith-based material, consider trying music or an audio book to seek God's face with your ears instead of your eyes.

FOR PRAYER AND REFLECTION

*At the end of the day, I'll pray about a way
in which I saw God's face.*

Would You Repeat That?

I will give them a heart that obeys and ears that hear; they will praise me in the land of their exile, and will remember my name.

BARUCH 2:31–32

Honestly, when did everyone start mumbling? And it's not just your family, friends, and coworkers; you find yourself asking baristas, the man who services your vehicle, and the delivery person to speak louder or more clearly. You hate to admit it, but you're starting to think this is probably about you, not them.

Some research indicates women who experience later menopause transitions or those on hormone replacement regimens are more likely to have hearing loss. If it's not one thing, it's another, right? Sometimes, consciously or unconsciously, we tune out conversations we consider unimportant. May we remember that when it comes to God, we've each been given "a heart that obeys and ears that hear," and use both.

ACTION

Someone you know likes to tell the same story—a tale of woe or a favorite memory—over and over again. The next time he or she starts in, hear that person, even if you don't understand every word.

FOR PRAYER AND REFLECTION

Today, I'll spend ten minutes in silence with Jesus.
Even if my ears don't hear, I have faith my soul will.

Ma'am? Me?

Do not fear, for I have redeemed you;
I have called you by name, you are mine.

ISAIAH 43:1

"Excuse me, ma'am." "Thank you, ma'am." "Do you need anything, ma'am?" The first few times you heard it, you didn't realize the person was talking to you. Ma'am is your grandmother; maybe, on a bad day, your mother. But you? You get that it's a term of respect, but when did you go from being miss or something else that doesn't make you seem quite so old?

Better ma'am than honey, sweetie, darling, or gorgeous from someone who doesn't know you well, right? But hearing ma'am still can be jarring. If the person is someone you're going to encounter again, consider telling him or her how you'd like to be addressed. Or, maybe just accept it with a smile, knowing that God always calls you beloved, for "you are mine."

ACTION

It's overwhelming, isn't it, to know that you are God's, redeemed by Jesus's death and resurrection? Remind yourself several times each day that you are God's, regardless of what anyone else may call you in love, indifference, or anger.

FOR PRAYER AND REFLECTION

Today, I'll make a list of all the nicknames I've had and pray for the people who called me by them with love.

Over the Hill?
Not Me!

Jealousy and anger shorten life,
and anxiety brings on premature old age.
Those who are cheerful and merry at table
will benefit from their food.

SIRACH 30:24–25

Some people like to joke about adding years. You are not among them. It's not that you're embarrassed by your age, but you don't see any reason to turn your next milestone birthday into an "over the hill" festival, complete with black streamers and balloons and canes and goofy spectacles. If age really is just a number, why do people find it so funny?

Having a sense of humor and perspective helps any situation. Maybe you're actually touchier than you want to admit about your age. Getting upset at small slights and being overly sensitive really isn't worth the emotional and mental investment, especially when others mean no ill by it. As Ben Sira wrote, "anxiety brings on premature old age," and who wants that?

ACTION

Have a chat with the Blessed Mother, who likely was in her forties at the wedding at Cana. Ask her to help you celebrate with others rather than attempt to put your own rules around birthday and anniversary parties and the like.

FOR PRAYER AND REFLECTION

Today, I'll pray for a blessing for my family and friends who like to make what they think are good-natured jokes about aging.

In the Wrong Places

Look to him, and be radiant;
so your faces shall never be ashamed.

PSALM 34:5

Last time you had your hair cut, the stylist asked if you wanted a lip or chin wax. And when you saw the mirror, you understood why. It's not like you have a full mustache or the beginnings of a goatee, but there's more hair on your face than you've noticed—or want. How bad is this going to get?

For some women, noticeable facial hair begins to appear during the transition to menopause. (This is also the time that hair on your head begins to thin, and that just doesn't seem fair.) Your options include the same old standbys as for your eyebrows and legs: tweeze, bleach, wax, electrolysis, or just live with it. Regardless, know that your face "shall never be ashamed" when you turn it to God with radiance.

ACTION

There's nothing wrong in taking pride in your personal grooming, and in particular wanting to look attractive at a time your hormones are all over the map. The same goes for your spiritual grooming. Maybe it's time for a refresh on your spiritual practice. Consider going to a different Mass or changing up your faith-based reading. It just might make you more radiant.

FOR PRAYER AND REFLECTION

Today I'll journal about the most faith-filled woman I know, what makes her beautiful, and what I can learn from her.

Well, My BFF Says...

The Lord created medicines out of the earth,
And the sensible will not despise them.

SIRACH 38:4

One of your friends swears her estrogen patch is all that keeps her fit to be around. Another one takes a prescription pill; a third is into herbal supplements. When you search on the internet, it's hard to know what's right for a woman in your situation: hot flashes that are annoying but not ruling your life, a few sleepless nights, a little brain fog.

Your transition into menopause is *your* transition. Every woman experiences this time a little differently, so just because something works for your friends doesn't mean it's right—or wrong—for you. Do talk to your doctor, but don't leave out the Master Physician. There's nothing wrong with exploring treatment options; after all, "the Lord created medicines out of the earth."

ACTION

God can be found in the good of all things in the world. As you navigate whether natural or other remedies are right for you, remain open to the possibility that God's thumbprint is on the work of reputable researchers and other medicine professionals.

FOR PRAYER AND REFLECTION

Lord, give me the wisdom and the courage to find and navigate the path that is right for me, physically and spiritually.

RESOURCES

You're not in this alone! Check out these resources
for information about the changes you're experiencing.

The **U.S. Department of Health & Human Services' Office on Women's Health** (https://www.womenshealth.gov/menopause/menopause-resources) offers a fact sheet, email updates, and more, including a helpline staffed on weekdays. Note that it does not provide medical advice or referrals.

The **American College of Obstetricians and Gynecologists** (acog.org/patient-resources/faqs/womens-health/the-menopause-years) has an extensive Q&A section for menopausal women.

The **U.S. Food & Drug Administration** (https://www.fda.gov/consumers/womens-health-topics/menopause) provides tips, free women's health publications, and other information.

The **U.S. Department of Health & Human Services' National Institute on Aging** (https://www.nia.nih.gov/health/what-menopause) offers clear, understandable information about the years leading up to and after menopause.

The **National Institutes of Health's MedlinePlus** resources on menopause include videos, research, and other resources.

The **Mayo Clinic** (https://www.mayoclinic.org/diseases-conditions/menopause/symptoms-causes/syc-20353397) provides insights on menopause symptoms, causes, and treatments.

The **North American Menopause Society** (http://www.menopause.org/for-women) has blog posts and video series.

The **National Institutes of Health's U.S. National Library of Medicine** (https://clinicaltrials.gov/search/open/condition=%22Hot+Flashes%22) offers information about ongoing research on hot flashes and other menopausal symptoms.

WebMD's Menopause Health Center (https://www.webmd.com/menopause/default.htm) includes news, videos, and blog posts.